Whine & Dine

Silvey-Jex

RAVETTE PUBLISHING

First published by Ravette Publishing 2009.

Ravette Publishing Limited
PO Box 876
Horsham
West Sussex RH12 9GH

ISBN: 978-1-84161-326-0

BUT IT CAN'T BE HORRIBLE SIR... OUR CHEF IS A FAMOUS T.V. CELEBRITY
SO IS BART SIMPSON - AND HE CAN'T COOK EITHER
SJ

MIND IF I SIT DOWN TO TAKE YOUR ORDER- MY FEET ARE KILLING ME
MENU
SJ.

IT'S ANGLO-ITALIAN 'FUSION' SIR, SPAGHETTI WITH YORKSHIRE PUDDING AND MUSHY PEAS
SJ

I DON'T UNDERSTAND IT. ANOTHER SATISFIED CUSTOMER.
SJ.

MY FRIEND HERE WOULD LIKE TO TRY THE WINE
SJ

MY COMPLIMENTS TO THE CHEF.... HE'S BEEN CONSTIPATED FOR DAYS.
TOILET

NOW-
THAT'S A DUMB WAITER
SJ.

CHEF WOULD LIKE TO APOLOGIZE FOR THE DODGY OYSTER
GENTLEMEN
SJ.

AN AMUSING LITTLE WINE FROM THE NAPA VALLEY. LIGHT, FRAGRANT YET WELL ROUNDED. VERY FRUITY WITH THAT HINT OF BLACK-BERRY LEAVING A SMOOTH & GENTLE AFTERTASTE THAT WON'T SCREW UP THE FLAVOUR OF SIR'S CHEESEBURGER
SJ

PARDON ME SIR BUT WE NEED THE BOUQUET GARNI BACK IN THE KITCHEN

AND WHAT WINE DO YOU SUGGEST WITH THE ALL-DAY BREAKFAST?
MENU
S.J.

OOOH!
"OKEY DOKEY
FISH BONES
CHOKEY"
MENU
SJ.

GOT TO BE RUDE TO WAITERS- TEACHES THEM RESPECT FOR THE CUSTOMER

I SAID!!!..
I THINK I
PREFERRED THE
OLD BUGGER WITH
THE VIOLIN
SJ

I KNOW MY WINE AND I'D SAY THAT ONE'S CORKED!
SJ

I THINK I CAN FEEL SOME CALAMARI TRYING TO ESCAPE

VELLY SOLLY. EXTRA PORTION OF EGG NOODLE PROVE TOO MUCH FOR TABLE
SJ.

WOULD SIR CARE TO TRY THE WINE?
CHATEAU MARGAUX
CHATEAU PETRUS
PICHON

WAITER THERE'S SOME SOUP IN MY FLY!

WHAT'S YOUR POISON TREV?
SJ.

WOULD SIR LIKE THE KIDNEYS DONE A LITTLE LONGER?
YES, AN HOUR ON A DIALYSIS MACHINE SHOULD DO IT

KIDS MENU
EYES BIGGER THAN HIS BELLY THAT ONE
SJ

SO... WHAT DID YOU HAVE FOR LUNCH TODAY THEN?
UM.. HOLD ON... I'LL JUST LOOK DOWN MY CARDIGAN AND SEE
SJ

CORRECT ME IF I'M WRONG BUT 'TOAD IN THE HOLE' IS MADE WITH SAUSAGES - NOT TOADS
SJ

NORMALLY SIR ONE JUST HAS A TASTE OF THE WINE... NOT THE ENTIRE BOTTLE
SJ.

SERVES YOU RIGHT FOR SAYING HIS PEA SOUP TASTES LIKE IT
SJ.

HOLD IT!... AREN'T YOU SUPPOSED TO SAY "GRACE"

CAREFUL SIR-THE PLATE IS VERY H....

THERE!
NOT MOVING NOW
IS IT?
SMACK!
SJ.

SO, WHAT'S YOUR VERDICT ON THE HOMEMADE LEMON AND TURNIP WINE?
SJ

NOW-BEFORE YOU SAY ANYTHING I DIDN'T COOK IT. OKAY?
SJ

WAITER!
THERE'S A BEAD IN
MY SOUP
SPECIALS
SJ

ARE YOU SUNNY SIDE UP, FRIES - MUSHIES A WAD AND BUILDERS WITH TWO?
ALL DAY BREAKFAST
FISH N CHIPS
I DON'T KNOW - WHAT DOES IT MEAN?
SJ

DON'T KNOW
WHY WE CAME HERE...
YOU KNOW CURRY
UPSETS ME!
YES

DON'T GET MUCH FOR YOUR MONEY DO YOU?
I DON'T HEAR ANYONE ELSE COMPLAINING - DO YOU SIR?
SJ.

MY FAULT!
I'M ALWAYS A BIT
HEAVY HANDED WITH
THE COGNAC
SJ.

HE'S ALLERGIC TO CAULIFLOWER. HE'LL BE ALRIGHT IN A MINUTE
!!?
SJ

HAD A 999 FROM TABLE 12. ACUTE DIARRHOEA AND VOMITING
MENU
EMERGENCY MEDICAL KIT
SJ